RECYCLE

AND

REMAKE

New things from old rubbish

The activities in this book are designed to help you make stuff from things that you might otherwise throw out. You will find the list of things you can rescue from the bin at the start of each project in the "from the rubbish" section. Collect your materials from what you already have at home and give them a clean before you use them. Please don't buy new rubbish to make the projects in this book!

Look out for this warning sign. It shows where you will need grown-up help.

DK Penguin Random House

Editor Hélène Hilton
Project Art Editor Charlotte Bull
Designer Sadie Thomas
Additional Illustration Kitty Glavin
Photographer Ruth Jenkinson
Fact Checker Lizzie Davey
Managing Editor Penny Smith
Managing Art Editor Mabel Chan
Producers, Pre-Production Sophie Chatellier, Abigail Maxwell
Producer Amy Knight
Picture Researcher Sakshi Saluja
Jacket Designer Rachael Parfitt Hunt
Jacket Co-ordinator Issy Walsh
Publishing Director Sarah Larter
Creative Director Helen Senior

First published in Great Britain in 2020 by
Dorling Kindersley Limited
80 Strand, London, WC2R 0RL

Copyright © 2020 Dorling Kindersley Limited
A Penguin Random House Company
10 9 8 7 6 5 4 3 2 1
001–315391–Mar/2020

A CIP catalogue record for this book is available from the British Library.
ISBN: 978-0-2413-9581-3

Printed and bound in China

A WORLD OF IDEAS:
SEE ALL THERE IS TO KNOW

www.dk.com

Contents

Planet health check

The Earth is our home. However, we humans don't always look after it properly. Understanding what we do wrong can help us fix it.

Landfills are huge places where rubbish is dumped then covered up or buried.

Wherever humans go, we change the natural environment. We've even left rubbish in space! To keep our planet healthy, we need to clean up after ourselves.

No such thing as "away"

When you throw something out, it doesn't really go away. Most rubbish is burned or dumped in a landfill, but some can be recycled. Recycling means making waste into something new!

Plastic pollution

Plastic waste takes thousands of years to break down into tiny bits. Unwanted plastic can hurt animals that get caught in it or eat it accidentally.

Food waste

Growing food for everyone on Earth takes up a lot of space and energy. On top of this, huge amounts of food are thrown away uneaten.

Global warming

Technology, factories, and vehicles need energy to work. Making this energy releases gases into the air that trap the Sun's heat. This means the planet is getting hotter and much harder to live on.

Fading forests

The world's forests are being cut down and burned to make room for cities and farms. Trees clean the gases that add to global warming. Without forests, the planet will get even hotter.

Life on Earth

As humans damage nature, other animals and plants struggle. Many are in danger of dying out altogether, and becoming extinct.

Let's heal the planet

Together, we can save the planet! The activities in this book are a good start. By giving rubbish a new life, you'll be reducing waste in the world.

The plastic problem

Plastic is very useful! We use it for everything from straws to buildings. The problem is that once it's made, plastic never really goes away.

Oil pump

Where does plastic come from?

Most plastic is made from oil, which takes millions of years to form deep inside the Earth. Oil is drilled out from under the ground or under the sea.

Oil

Where does plastic go?

Some plastic can be recycled into new objects, but this only works a few times. Most plastic rubbish is burned, releasing harmful gases into the air. Some is dumped in landfill or at sea.

Sea of plastic

Lots of plastic ends up in the seas and oceans, either by accident or because people dump it there. Sea animals such as dolphins, birds, and turtles can get caught in it.

Put rubbish in the bin to stop it from being blown into rivers and the sea.

Sea birds and other animals have been found with plastic in their stomachs. Swallowing plastic hurts them from the inside. It also doesn't leave room in their stomachs for real food, so they die.

Scientists are inventing alternatives to plastic. For example, they have made water pods from seaweed that could replace plastic bottles.

Plastic planters

Don't throw out all your plastic bottles! Try turning them into new homes for your favourite plants.

What will you put in your planter? See pages 32 and 33 to learn how to make your own compost.

From the rubbish
Plastic bottles

Extra bits
Scissors
Acrylic paint
Paintbrushes
String

1

⚠️

Save the middle part! You can use it to make a bee hotel on the next page.

Cut the top and the bottom off a bottle. Both pieces can be used to make planters.

2

Decorate the planters by painting on a pattern or picture. You might need more than one coat of paint to make the colours pop!

For hanging planters, use scissors to make two or three holes around the rim of the planter. Knot string through each hole, then hang from a hook. ⚠️

Welcome to the Bee Hotel!

Make a bee-rilliant hotel to get your garden or local park buzzing with life! Look in your rubbish to help you decide which of these bee hotels to make.

Vacancies!

Plastic straws are bad for nature. Squeeze them in tightly so they can't fall out and blow away.

From the rubbish

Old plant pots, or plastic cups, or the middle of a plastic bottle

Old straws

Dry grass

Newspaper or scrap paper

Cardboard

Extra bits

Scissors

String

Cut off the top and bottom of a plastic bottle. Use the middle for your bee hotel.

Fill the middle part of a plastic bottle with your old or used straws to make bee bedrooms.

Roll up bits of newspaper or scrap paper to make little bee-sized tubes.

Hang up your hotel somewhere sheltered from the rain and wind.

Different types of bees need different sized bedrooms.

How do bees help the planet?

Bees are pollinators - they buzz from flower to flower, spreading pollen. When a flower receives pollen, it can make seeds, which then grow into new plants. Without bees, many plants would disappear.

Roll up cardboard in a swirl. Fill the gaps with dry grass so it doesn't move around.

Rescued pencil pots

Rescue a used plastic cup from the rubbish! You can turn it into a colourful pencil pot.

From the rubbish

Plastic cup or yoghurt pot

Old yarn, strips of fabric, or strips of plastic bags

Extra bits

Ruler

Pen

Scissors

Glue

Try weaving strips of plastic bags.

1 Ask a grown-up to help you measure the side of the cup with a ruler and draw lines to divide it into sections.

Split the cup into an odd number of sections, such as 7, 9, 11, or 13 sections.

2 Carefully cut along the lines. Leave a small gap uncut at the base.

Make a plait

Tie three lengths of fabric into a knot at one end. Move the outer colour over the top and between the other two. Take turns moving the left colour and the right colour into the middle until the plait is long enough, then tie it off.

Keep practising!

Glue plaits to the top and bottom to decorate.

3 Tie a knot in the end of your fabric and push it between two sections. Weave it in and out of the sections around the cup.

4 Keep weaving until you get to the top! To finish, or to change colour, tie a little knot in your fabric inside the cup.

Push the fabric down as you go.

Planet of trees

Trees provide homes for animals, clean the air we breathe, and keep our planet healthy. However, forests around the world are disappearing.

Forests are home to plants and animals that can live nowhere else. As the forests are cut down, some plants and animals will disappear forever.

Plants take in carbon dioxide gas from the air and turn it into oxygen. Carbon dioxide traps heat, making our planet hotter. By using it, trees help fight the climate crisis.

Trees soak up water when it rains, and release any they don't need through their leaves as water vapour. This helps keep the air cool.

Over half the world's forests are already gone.

The main reason forests are destroyed is to make space for towns and farms.

Growing on trees

We use things from trees every day. Many of our favourite fruits and most important medicines come from trees. Wood, from a tree's trunks and branches, is a great material to make homes, furniture, paper, and cardboard.

To make paper or cardboard from a tree, wood is chopped up into tiny bits and mixed with water. This makes pulp, which is then dried into sheets of paper or card.

Recycled bookmarks

Save trees by making your very own recycled paper. Once you've mushed the paper up into a pulp, you can dry it into sheets and cut it into bookmarks.

From the rubbish

Scrap paper (newspaper, used gift wrap, or junk mail)

Extra bits

Bowl

Warm water

Tray

Tea towel

Decorations (petals, hay, confetti)

Sponge

Scissors

Ribbon

1 Start breaking down your scrap paper by ripping it up into little pieces into a bowl.

2

Pour warm water into the bowl, covering the paper, and let it soak for around half an hour.

Squeeze!

3

It's time to get messy! Squeeze and rip the soaked paper until it feels gooey. Paper mush is called pulp.

Squash! Mush!

Turn the page to make sheets of paper.

Tip!

For rainbow sheets, make pulp from scrap paper of different colours.

4

Pour a thin layer of pulp into a tray over a tea towel. Add decoration to the pulp if you like, then fold the towel over the top. Sponge up the water through the towel, squashing the pulp as you go.

Tea towel

Paper pulp

Soak up the water.

Squash!

Press!

5

Leave the sheet to dry for a couple of days, then gently lift it out of the tray.

6 Cut your new sheets into bookmarks. Add a ribbon to make an extra fancy bookmark!

What decorations will you add? You could try flower petals, hay, or confetti.

Seeded shapes

If you have leftover pulp, you can make little seeded shapes with it. Place the pulp inside a cookie cutter and push it up to the edges.

Gently lift the cutter away, squash on some seeds, then leave the shapes to dry for a few days.

Plant the seeded shapes in soil and compost, then water. The paper will break down and the seeds will slowly grow.

Two things to make with
a shoe box

A shoe box isn't just great to store shoes in. Here are two fun games you could make.

I want to play!

Bead maze

Turn the **shoe box lid** into a maze! Move the lid from side to side to roll the beads from start to finish.

Start here

Make the maze walls from bits of scrap cardboard or old straws. Stick them in place with paper tape or glue.

End here

You could try painting your maze and beads.

Shadow theatre

Use the **base of the shoe box** to make a mini shadow puppet theatre. What story will you tell?

Use a torch or a lamp to light the shadow theatre from behind.

Baking paper

Make character puppets from black card and sticks to use in your theatre.

Carefully cut a rectangle out of the bottom of the box. Stick baking paper to the inside.

Tip! Decorate your theatre with painted card curtains.

Cardboard castle

With a little imagination, you can turn a boring old cardboard box into something completely magical.

1 Draw these shapes on cardboard with a ruler. The bigger you make them, the bigger your castle will be!

x 2

These two pieces will be the front and back walls of your castle.

These slits should be the same thickness as the cardboard.

x 1

This piece will be the middle wall.

x 4

These four pieces will be the castle's floors.

2 Cut out the castle shapes, windows, and slits along the dotted lines. Paint on extra decorations if you want.

3 Build your castle! Start with the middle and outer walls, then add the floors.

Party piñata

Make this special party game from a cardboard box. It doesn't need to be very neat, as you'll soon be bashing it open to get to the yummy treasure inside!

From the rubbish
Cardboard boxes
Used wrapping paper

Extra bits
Pen
Scissors
Ruler
Paper tape
Sweets (foil or paper-wrapped sweets are best)
String

Tip!
Most plastic sticky tape can't be recycled. Use paper tape to make your piñata so you can recycle it after your party.

1

Draw the shape of your piñata on the cardboard and carefully cut it out. Draw around the cutout to make a second, identical shape and cut that out too.

2

Use a ruler to draw long rectangles on another piece of cardboard and cut them out. These will be the sides of the piñata.

3

Stick the strips all the way around to the edges of the shape with tape. Bend the cardboard to fit the shape and trim any bits that are too long.

4

Fill the piñata with sweets! Then stick the lid down with more tape.

5

Cut strips of old
wrapping paper. Snip
little notches in the
paper to make it ruffly.

6

Decorate your piñata
by sticking the ruffly paper
on in layers using more paper
tape. Keep going until you
can't see the cardboard.

7 ⚠️ Ask a grown-up to poke a hole in the piñata to hang it up. Use strong string as it's about to get bashed!

Party time!

Take turns with your party guests bashing the piñata with a soft bat! Be careful not to bash your friends.

Add a tassel tail if you have extra wrapping paper.

Once the piñata breaks open, all the sweets will tumble out!

Fresh from the farm

There are nearly eight billion people
on the planet, and they all need to eat!
We need to think carefully about how we can
grow enough food without harming the Earth.

Clearing forests

Farming is the main reason forests are being
burned and cut down. Humans clear trees to
make fields for farm animals to live in and to
grow animal feed. Space is also cleared to
grow crops, such as palm trees for palm oil.

Palm oil is used in
lots of prepared
foods and products,
such as bread and
toiletries.

Palm oil is called
many different names,
including vegetable
oil, vegetable fat,
and glyceryl.

Palm oil farm

Homegrown food

Food grown on the other side of the world is often transported to other countries by plane or boat, which pollutes the air and sea. Check labels to find food that was grown locally, or try to grow your own.

Eat more veggies!

Farm animals need lots of space, water, and energy to feed and grow. Humans can help the planet by eating more plants and less meat, so we don't need as many farm animals.

Try some yummy new plant-based recipes!

Cows fart out a gas called methane, which contributes to global warming. Unfortunately, cows fart a lot... and there are more than a billion of them in the world.

More than half of all the mammals in the world are farm animals, such as cows and sheep. Humans make up another third. Less than one in every 20 mammals in the world is a wild animal.

Chemical farming

Some farmers use chemicals to get rid of insects that could eat their crops. But these chemicals often spread out into the environment and harm other plants and animals too. That's why other farmers choose to use fewer or no chemicals.

Seven out of every ten birds in the world are farm birds, such as chickens.

New plants from food scraps

Instead of throwing out your food
scraps, give your fruit and vegetables
a chance of an exciting new life.

Celery

Celery will grow new
crunchy stalks if it
gets plenty of water
and sunshine.

Garlic

Suspend a garlic clove in water
with cocktail sticks. Within a few days
it should sprout a stem and little roots.
Plant it in soil and compost to regrow
a whole new garlic bulb.

Carrots

Carrot tops won't grow new carrots, but they
can grow new leaves. Place them in the sun in
a shallow dish of water. Once the leaves start
to grow, plant the carrot tops in soil and
compost to make a pretty potted plant.

What do plants need to live?

Plants need light and water. They use their leaves to soak up light from the Sun. They suck up water from the soil around their roots.

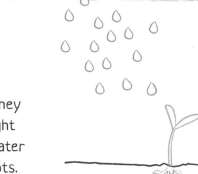

Lettuce

Lettuce will grow new leaves if you leave the stem in a little water in a sunny place.

Spring onions

Save your spring onion roots to regrow them. Set them up in a glass of water, then plant them in soil and compost once the roots have started to grow.

Avocados

Avocados have a big, round pit inside of them. Suspend it in water until it grows a root and a leafy stem. Plant it in soil and compost. After a few years you will have an avocado tree.

Fruits have pips, pits, or stones inside them. These are seeds that new plants can grow from. Plant different seeds in soil and compost to see what happens!

Food for plants

Some food scraps are no good for us to eat, but we can use them in other ways. Break them down into compost. Compost is a super food for plants!

In your compost

For your compost to break down properly, you'll need the right mix of "brown" and "green" things. Try to use about half and half "brown" and "green" waste.

Paper and newspaper

Dry sticks and leaves

These count as "brown" things.

Cardboard

Dry grass

To make your compost, you'll need a compost bin in your garden or a mini compost bin on your balcony. Pick a sheltered place in the shade.

Little bugs might come and live in your compost. They help to break it down.

Potato peelings

Apple skin

Green leaves and grass

Banana skins

These count as "green" things.

Fruit peelings

Vegetables peelings

Wait a few months for the scraps to break down. The compost should be brown, without any bits in it. Mix your compost with soil to help new plants grow.

Eggshell seed pots

Empty eggshells work well as tiny, natural plant pots. Use your homemade compost to grow something new.

From the rubbish

Empty eggshells

Extra bits

Compost and soil

Spoon

Seeds (we used cress but try it with any seeds)

Water

Plant pot or jar

1 Fill the eggshells with a mix of soil and compost. Pat it down, leaving a little space at the top.

2 Carefully sprinkle the seeds over the soil.

Soil

Seeds

3 Cover the seeds with a little more soil and compost, then gently pat down again.

How do plants help the Earth?

Plants don't breathe like we do, but they do take in an invisible gas called carbon dioxide from the air. Carbon dioxide makes the planet hotter, which is bad for the environment. Growing more plants helps to fight against global warming and the climate crisis!

4

Place your eggs in a sunny place. Water the soil, then wait.

Repot other plants in jars of soil, such as your spring onion scraps from page 31.

5

within a day or two, you should see little green cress shoots.

When the shoots appear, gently crack the eggshell, then place the whole thing in a bigger pot of soil and compost. The shell will break down and feed your cress, and the roots will grow through the little cracks.

Our clothes

Have you ever thought about where your clothes come from or how they were made? The clothes we buy have a big impact on our planet.

Take a look at the label in your clothing. What material is it made from?

What is fabric?

Fabric is what clothes are made from. It can be made from man-made materials or natural things like plants.

Man-made fabrics, such as polyester, are usually made of plastic. When these fabrics are washed, tiny bits of plastic fall off and are carried away to the sea.

Natural fabrics, such as cotton, are made from plants, which can need a lot of water to grow.

To get the most out of your clothes, wear them until you grow out of them. You can also use fabric from damaged clothes to make something new.

Too much to wear

Billions of clothes are made every year, but not all are sold and many are thrown away. Some people also throw out their clothes when they get bored of them.

Picked cotton

Many people who make clothes, including some children, are very poor. They work long hours in hot fields and in factories.

Cotton

What happens to the clothes?

Clothes that are binned often end up in landfill. Instead of throwing away clothes that are too small, give them to other people who will wear them, or to a charity shop. That way fewer new clothes will need to be made.

Wax wrap

Cheer up your snack with this colourful beeswax food wrap. Use it instead of cling film to reduce plastic waste. You can reuse it over and over again!

From the rubbish
Scrap piece of cotton fabric

Extra bits
Ironing board

Baking paper

Beeswax bars

Cheese grater

Iron

Scissors

String (to tie up your wrap)

1 ⚠️

Grated beeswax

Baking paper

Put the cotton on an ironing board, on top of a big sheet of baking paper. Carefully grate beeswax onto the cotton, leaving space around the edges.

Beeswax bars

2

Place a second sheet
of baking paper on top.
Ask a grown-up to help
you iron the cotton until
you can see the wax
melting into it.

3

Leave the wrap
to cool, then
peel it off the
baking paper.

Cut off the
unwaxed edges
of your wrap.

Start wrapping your
lunches and snacks!
When your wrap gets
dirty, wipe it clean
with a sponge.

Three things to make with
fabric scraps

Even if you take really good care of your clothes, they will eventually get worn out. You can turn any fabric scraps into something cool.

Denim pencil pot

If your jeans get too short, cut the legs off and turn them into summer shorts. Then use the legs to make these little pots.

Turn the cut-off leg inside out. Bunch up one end, then tie it off with an elastic band. Turn the leg back the right way round, tucking the bunched up end inside.

Roll down the top of the pencil pot to help it stand up.

Friendship bracelet

Cut some skinny strips of fabric to plait into colourful friendship bracelets. Choose your favourite colours, your team colours, or just colours that look nice together.

Look at page 13 to remind yourself how to do a plait, then tie the ends around your wrist with a knot.

Some people say that if you wear a friendship bracelet until it breaks off, your wish will come true!

Forever bangle

To make a fancy bracelet, use an old plastic bottle and fabric scraps to make a bangle. This way, you're recycling two things at once!

Cut a ring out of a plastic bottle. Wrap fabric scraps around the ring, tucking the end under as you go. If it doesn't stay, glue the fabric to stop it unravelling Keep wrapping until you can't see the plastic anymore.

41

Favourite tote bag

If your favourite T-shirt is wearing out, turn it into a great tote bag! Carry it around in a pocket so you never have to use a plastic carrier bag again.

1 Cut the arms off your T-shirt to make the handles. Cut off a semicircle under the neck.

These will be the bag's handles.

From the rubbish

An old T-shirt

Extra bits

Scissors

2 Turn the T-shirt inside out. Snip slits along the bottom, leaving long thin strips of fabric that you can tie into knots.

3 Work your way along the bottom tying the fabric strips into double knots. This will bring the sides of the T-shirt together.

Zero-waste shops are places where you can buy groceries without any packaging. Shoppers bring their own reusable bags and containers to cut down on waste.

what will you fill your bag with?

4 Turn the T-shirt the right way round and enjoy your new bag!

It's an emergency!

Global warming is the biggest challenge facing our planet. The Earth is steadily getting hotter, and as humans burn more energy this is happening faster and faster.

We can save the planet!

Burning energy

Lots of the energy we use to make things work comes from burning oil and coal. They are burned to make electricity and used as fuel for cars and planes. This releases gases, such as carbon dioxide, that trap heat close to the planet.

To stop the Earth getting hotter, we have to cut down on harmful gases. We should also plant a lot more trees to get rid of the extra carbon dioxide already in the air.

Clean energies

The power of sunlight, wind, and moving water can also make electricity. These are clean energies because they don't harm the planet.

Global crisis

Even if the Earth is getting hotter, the weather where you are might not change that much. Global warming affects the world overall, even if you can't see it yourself.

As weather becomes more extreme, there are more droughts and fires, and also more floods.

But we need to change the way we live, and change it fast. That's why this is a CLIMATE EMERGENCY!

Ice that hasn't melted for millions of years is melting now. If it continues, sea levels will rise and flooded land will disappear into the sea.

Animals like polar bears that need ice to live on have nowhere to go and can't find food.

The seas are also heating up. Even getting a tiny bit hotter kills coral reefs, which provide homes for billions of animals.

Throughout the world, many people are working very hard to save the planet. **Turn over to see what you can do!**

Little changes make a big difference

Switch lights off to save electricity.

Earth is the only planet where humans, animals, and plants can live. Here are some ways you and your family can help take care of it.

Walk, cycle, or take the bus to

Check that the energy you use at home is clean and green.

Eat less meat and dairy to reduce the space and water used for farming.

Plant a tree to fight global warming.

46

Work together

There are lots of things you can do by yourself, but we can do even more together. Make your voice heard by writing to politicians who can make big changes, or join an environment group with your family.

Really think about the things you buy. How and where were they made? Do you really need to buy more?

cut down on car pollution.

Take the train instead of flying to make less carbon dioxide.

Buy second hand to reuse, rather than buying new things.

Choose natural fabrics and wash your clothes less often, to stop tiny bits of plastic getting into the ocean.

Turn things off

instead of leaving them on standby, to save electricity.

wash clothes at a lower temperature to save energy.

Use reusable containers such as cups, jars, and bags, to cut out single-use plastic.

Index

B, C

Bead maze 20
Bee hotel 10-11
Bookmarks 16-19
Bracelet 41
Chemicals 29
Clothes 36-37, 40-41, 42-43
Compost 8, 30-31, 32-33, 34-35

E, F

Electricity 44, 46-47
Energy 5, 29, 44-45, 46-47
Farming 5, 15, 28-29
Forests 5, 14-15, 28

G

Gases 5, 6, 14, 29, 35 44-45
Global warming 5, 14, 29, 44-45

O, P, R

Ocean 6-7, 45
Paint 8-9, 20, 21, 22-23
Paper 10-11, 15, 16-19, 24-27, 32
Pencil pot 12-13, 40
Piñata, party 24-27
Plait 13, 41
Recycling 4-5, 6, 16, 24

S, T, W

Sea 6-7, 29, 45
Shadow theatre 21
Shoe box 20-21
Straws 6, 10-11, 20
Trees 5, 14-15, 16, 28
Wax wrap 38-39

DK would like to thank

Becky Walsh, Brandie Tully-Scott, and Celine Ka Wing Lau for craft and photoshoot assistance, James Mitchem and Seeta Parmar for editorial help.

Acknowledgements

The publisher would like to thank the following for their kind permission to reproduce their photographs:

(Key: a-above; b-below/bottom; c-centre; f-far; l-left; r-right; t-top)

2-3 Dreamstime.com: Praewpailin PhonSri (Background). 3 Fotolia: Eric Isselee (bl). 4 Alamy Stock Photo: Jupiterimages (cra). Dreamstime.com: Alfio Scisetti / Scisettialfio (br); Vchalup (cl). iStockphoto.com: Robert Pleško (bl). 4-5 Dreamstime.com: Praewpailin PhonSri (Background). 5 Fotolia: Eric Isselee (cr). 6-7 Dreamstime.com: Praewpailin PhonSri (Background). 6 Dreamstime.com: Photka (cb); Alfio Scisetti / Scisettialfio (cra, crb). 7 123RF.com: (clb/Ban sign); Aleksey Poprugin (bc). Alamy Stock Photo: Paulo Oliveira (tr). Dorling Kindersley: Natural History Museum, London (clb). Dreamstime.com: Onyxprj (clb/Plastic bottles); Alfio Scisetti / Scisettialfio (cla, cl, c, cb). 10-11 Dreamstime.com: Praewpailin PhonSri (Background). 14 Dreamstime.com: Galyna Andrushko (cla). Fotolia: Eric Isselee (cb). 14-15 Dreamstime.com: Praewpailin PhonSri (Background). 15 123RF.com: Eric Isselee / isselee (clb); Picsfive (crb). Dreamstime.com: Damian Palus (fclb); Yotrak (tr). 16-17 Dreamstime.com: Praewpailin PhonSri (Background). 18-19 Dreamstime.com: Praewpailin PhonSri (Background). 20 Dreamstime.com: Oleksandr Shyripa (cra). 20-21 Dreamstime.com: Praewpailin PhonSri (Background). 21 Fotolia: Matthew Cole (ca). 22-23 Dreamstime.com: Praewpailin PhonSri (Background).

24-25 Dreamstime.com: Praewpailin PhonSri (Background). 26-27 Dreamstime.com: Praewpailin PhonSri (Background). 28-29 Dreamstime.com: Praewpailin PhonSri (Background). 28 Dreamstime.com: Grafner (crb). iStockphoto.com: YuSnizam (cb). 29 123RF.com: Eric Isselee / isselee (cl, cra, ca, cb, cr); Sauletas (clb). Dreamstime.com: Ekaterina Semenova / EkaterinaSemenova (tl). 32-33 Dreamstime.com: Praewpailin PhonSri (Background). 34-35 Dreamstime.com: Praewpailin PhonSri (Background). 36-37 Dreamstime.com: Praewpailin PhonSri (Background). iStockphoto.com: Foto-Ianniello (c). 37 Dreamstime.com: GilleSpaire (tr). iStockphoto.com: Neenawat (cr). 38-39 Dreamstime.com: Praewpailin PhonSri (Background). 40-41 Dreamstime.com: Praewpailin PhonSri (Background). 42-43 Dreamstime.com: Praewpailin PhonSri (Background). 44-45 Dreamstime.com: Praewpailin PhonSri (Background). 44 123RF.com: AlphaSpirit (br). iStockphoto.com: Plherrera (cl). 45 Dorling Kindersley: Jerry Young (cb). iStockphoto.com: Milehightraveler (tr). 46 123RF.com: Eric Isselee / isselee (clb, cb). 46-47 Dreamstime.com: Praewpailin PhonSri (Background). 47 123RF.com: Natthawut Panyosaeng / aopsan (br). Dreamstime.com: Gv1961 (cra). 48 Dreamstime.com: Praewpailin PhonSri (Background)

Cover images: Front: 123RF.com: RoyStudio, Roman Samokhin ca; Back: 123RF.com: RoyStudio

All other images © Dorling Kindersley
For further information see: www.dkimages.com